SPOTLIGHT
ON
WORDS

SPOTLIGHT
ON
WORDS

Phonic wordsearch puzzles and activities
to help the development of spelling skills

First edition published by
The Robinswood Press 1994

Designed by
Catalyst Ltd Birmingham England

Printed by Wynstones Press and G.S. Print

The Robinswood Press

Stourbridge England
ISBN 1 869981 51 0

CONTENTS

ABOUT THE AUTHOR

Gillian Aitken M.A., P.G.C.E., R.S.A.Dip., T.E.F.L., A.M.B.D.A.

Gillian Aitken trained originally as an English teacher, and taught in schools for a number of years. More recently she has concentrated on areas in teaching English where a specialised approach is required. These have included teaching pupils with Special Needs, teaching pupils where English is a Second Language, and in teaching English as a Foreign Language.

Ms Aitken therefore has a unique range of expertise gained practically in both the UK and abroad, and through further academic study. This background has provided Ms Aitken with perfect opportunities to develop exercises - such as these wordsearch activities - which meet the educationalist's requirement to build spelling and reading skills, whilst the pupil can become engrossed in the challenge and enjoyment of the exercises themselves.

Ms Aitken lives in Sussex and is an Associate member of the British Dyslexia Association and continues to teach English in a number of areas, including adult literacy work with the Dyslexia Institute.

FOREWORD

An effective teacher enables students to learn in their own way and independently. Once a student has grasped a new teaching point, it must be practised over and over again until the point is secure. For a busy specialist teacher this means hours spent making new work sheets to present the same idea in yet another way. The student should not become bored before the point has been thoroughly learnt.

Gillian Aitken's worksheets provide a welcome additional resource for such teachers as well as for parents. The wordsearch puzzles are certainly an enjoyable way to reinforce phonic groups. They could, indeed, be used alone before a student is ready to tackle the related sentences as additional follow up work. The presentation is particularly clear - even younger children will easily understand what has to be done.

These worksheets will be valuable for all students following a structured spelling course. Teachers working with Specific Learning Difficulty students will need to read Gillian Aitken's introduction carefully to ensure that their approach is multisensory, and that students say words and sentences out loud. She also gives useful pointers for encouraging the students to think for themselves and for using memory techniques. Both will be essential ingredients of the lesson.

Felicity Patterson, Training Principal for the South East, The Dyslexia Institute.

INTRODUCTION

The wordsearch puzzles in Spotlight on Words are designed primarily for pupils with Specific Learning Difficulties who are following a structured spelling programme.

They can, of course, be used with any pupil who would benefit from a systematic, phonic approach to spelling. The puzzles are therefore a useful additional resource for the non-specialist teacher or parent who needs practice material to improve a child's spelling which is more 'digestible' than mere lists of words to learn. The puzzle element is obviously appealing to most children.

The wordseach puzzles are divided into three sections. Puzzles 1-16 give practice in spelling choices for long vowels and diphthongs; puzzles 17-24 focus on vowel sounds spelt with 'r'; and puzzles 25-30 illustrate certain endings after short vowels in one-syllable words.

For dyslexic pupils, it is assumed that each spelling choice will already have been introduced and practised through multi-sensory teaching methods. The wordsearch puzzles will provide extra practice, and can be used as immediate reinforcement of a new teaching point, or revision at a later date. Once the pupil is familiar with the format, he or she should be able to work fairly independently.

The worksheets give practice in different skill areas. First, finding the words themselves involves visual discrimination. Some of the target words in the word squares are names, for example, people or places, so pupils should be encouraged to look for capital letters. Secondly, as each word is discovered, it has to be written in the alphabetical list beside the square. This obviously gives useful practice in alphabetical sequencing.

A cue-word is illustrated on each puzzle page to the right of the word list. The teacher can use this illustration as a way into each puzzle by asking the child to name the picture and, if possible, spell the designated cue-word. After the target phonic pattern has been identified in this way, the child can be asked to find the cue-word in the puzzle and then write it in the alphabetical word list. As the child is now alert to the word-pattern, he or she will then be ready to complete the puzzle with minimal help from the teacher.

In most wordsearch puzzles, there will be two or more words beginning with the same letter and perhaps having the same number of letters, for example, 'lake' and 'late' in number 1. It does not matter if pupils do not sequence such words correctly as they write the words in the list, but some useful alphabet work could be done as a follow-up by focusing on words which begin with the same letter and deciding how they should be sequenced. Puzzle number 23, for example, has five words beginning with 's' blends or digraphs which differ only in the second letter of each word.

Finally, the fill-in-the-blank exercise at the bottom of each sheet is a 'read-and-think' exercise where contextual clues in each sentence will point to the choice of one word only to fill each blank. The emphasis in the last exercise is on meaning, an important element sometimes overlooked when teaching spelling. Impulsive guessing should be discouraged. Some of the sentences are much easier to complete than others. Pupils should be encouraged to do the more obvious ones first, and work out the more difficult ones by process of elimination. When copying words from the alphabetical list to the sentences, pupils should employ the 'Look-Say-Cover-Write-Check' routine to ensure that the words have been copied correctly.

On completion, each puzzle can be used as the basis for memory work if desired. This could be carried out as a game. For example, pupils could be given a time limit to recall as many words as possible from the puzzle they have just completed, and points could be awarded for the total number of words recalled, with bonus points for correct spelling and correct sequencing. Techniques for remembering lists of words using association or other methods could also be introduced or practised as a follow-up activity.

Because so many dyslexic pupils suffer from directional confusion, the words in the wordsearch puzzles do not go upwards, backwards or diagonally as in many commercial puzzles. They only go ACROSS and DOWN.

In several puzzles, a smaller word can be found inside a larger one. For example, in puzzle number 7 we have 'cream' inside 'scream', and in puzzle number 16 we have 'right' inside 'bright' and 'fright'. When this happens, the smaller word will have its own place in the puzzle and should be ignored inside a longer word. Generally speaking, words only overlap by one letter. Confusion can be avoided if pupils find all the words beginning with a consonant blend first. If a word begins with a 2 - or 3 - consonant blend, it is indicated in the alphabetical list. The teacher could, in fact, put an asterisk against the words which should be found first to avoid possible confusion.

Most of the target words in the squares are one-syllable words. Where two-syllable words are included, the first syllable of the word is given in the alphabetical list. Several two-syllable words are included in puzzles 22, 23 and 24 ('-ire', '-are' and '-ore' words). In these puzzles, less help is given with words beginning with consonant blends in that only the initial letter is given.

The wordsearch puzzles have not been designed for a specific age range, but to slot in with a structured spelling programme. I have used them successfully with 9 to 12 year-olds. They have proved very popular and motivating, and pupils compete with each other to be the first to finish! Once pupils become used to the format and have tried out one or two, they can generally complete a puzzle in less than thirty minutes.

Gillian Aitken M.A., P.G.C.E., R.S.A.Dip., T.E.F.L., A.M.B.D.A.

WORDSEARCH PUZZLE - NUMBER 1 | a-e

b	w	a	k	e	d	p	t	l
m	a	d	e	n	f	h	k	a
i	w	D	a	v	e	g	v	t
s	a	e	e	s	c	a	p	e
c	d	o	e	a	r	t	l	q
a	e	g	j	m	a	e	J	u
k	l	a	k	e	n	i	a	w
e	c	r	a	t	e	m	n	y
q	n	a	m	e	r	x	e	j

In this wordsearch puzzle you should be able to find 14 'a-e' words. Two of the words are names. Each time you find a word with these letters, write it down - in the right place - in the list below.

1 c _ _ _   8 l _ _ _

2 cr _ _ _   9 l _ _ _

3 cr _ _ _   10 m _ _ _

4 D _ _ _ _   11 n _ _ _

5 es _ _ _ _   12 s _ _ _

6 g _ _ _   13 w _ _ _

7 J _ _ _   14 w _ _ _

a-e

When you have completed your list of 14 'a-e' words, use each one, once only, to complete the blanks in the sentences below.

1   If you _____ up _____ you will miss the bus.

2   _____ _____ a big chocolate _____ in her

    cooking lesson.

3   If you forget to shut the _____, the dog will

    _____.

4   In Tom's class there were two other boys with the

    _____ _____.

5   _____ took off his shoes and socks and

    _____d into the _____.

6   The _____ lifted the heavy _____ off the ship.

WORDSEARCH PUZZLE - NUMBER 2   i-e

a	s	l	i	d	e	j	t	y
b	i	t	e	r	s	p	i	h
r	i	d	e	w	f	b	m	r
i	b	s	u	M	i	k	e	i
d	i	v	h	o	v	s	c	p
e	k	w	i	f	e	d	n	e
g	e	j	d	r	u	o	i	v
k	i	t	e	x	p	i	n	e
r	w	h	i	t	e	t	e	h

In this wordsearch puzzle you should be able to find 15 'i-e' words. One of the words is a boy's name. Each time you find a word with these letters, write it down - in the right place - in the list below.

1 b _ _ _

2 b _ _ _

3 br _ _ _

4 f _ _ _

5 h _ _ _

6 k _ _ _

7 M _ _ _

8 n _ _ _

9 p _ _ _

10 r _ _ _

11 r _ _ _

12 sl _ _ _

13 t _ _ _

14 wh _ _ _

15 w _ _ _

i-e

When you have completed your list of 15 'i-e' words, use each one, once only, to complete the blanks in the sentences below.

1 The children spent a long _____ going up and down the _____.

2 The bell for school went at _____ minutes to _____.

3 The _____ wore a long _____ dress.

4 Tom's mother told him not to _____ his _____ on the main road.

5 The _____ got stuck in the tall _____ tree.

6 The man told his _____ to _____ the Christmas presents under the bed.

7 _____ took a _____ of the _____ apple.

b	a	s	l	o	p	e	f	i
r	w	o	k	e	c	b	k	m
o	c	d	p	h	o	n	e	g
k	n	o	s	e	d	q	r	s
e	P	d	o	z	e	a	o	m
R	o	m	e	g	h	x	d	o
b	p	f	l	n	o	t	e	k
d	e	z	m	o	l	e	c	e
h	s	t	o	v	e	u	j	n

In this wordsearch puzzle you should be able to find 15 'o-e' words. One of the words is the name of a city, another is the head of a Church. Each time you find a word with these letters, write it down - in the right place - in the list below.

1 **br** _ _ _

2 **c** _ _ _

3 **d** _ _ _

4 **h** _ _ _

5 **m** _ _ _

6 **n** _ _ _

7 **n** _ _ _

8 **ph** _ _ _

9 **P** _ _ _

10 **r** _ _ _

11 **R** _ _ _

12 **sl** _ _ _

13 **sm** _ _ _

14 **st** _ _ _

15 **w** _ _ _

o-e

When you have completed your list of 15 'o-e' words, use each one, once only, to complete the blanks in the sentences below.

1 A _____ is a small animal which lives in a _____.

2 David _____ his _____ when he fell off his bike.

3 The _____ lives in _____, the capital city of Italy.

4 Thick, grey _____ was coming from the _____ because the wood was wet.

5 We could not understand the _____ because it was written in _____ .

6 She _____d for a short time and then _____ up when the _____ rang.

7 The boy _____ his bike down the _____ at top speed.

WORDSEARCH PUZZLE - NUMBER 4 u-e

f	l	u	t	e	r	a	p	n
r	c	o	n	f	u	s	e	z
e	u	m	t	g	d	k	r	t
f	b	J	u	n	e	q	f	u
u	e	m	b	d	j	w	u	n
s	D	u	e	f	r	y	m	e
e	u	l	L	u	k	e	e	s
h	k	e	j	r	u	l	e	x
p	e	x	c	u	s	e	v	r

In this wordsearch puzzle you should be able to find 14 'u-e' words. Three of the words are names, one of a boy, one of a month and one of a titled person. Each time you find a word with these letters, write it down - in the right place - in the list below.

1 **con** _ _ _ _   8 **m** _ _ _ _

2 **c** _ _ _ _   9 **per** _ _ _ _

3 **D** _ _ _   10 **re** _ _ _ _

4 **ex** _ _ _ _   11 **r** _ _ _

5 **fl** _ _ _   12 **r** _ _ _

6 **J** _ _ _   13 **t** _ _ _ _

7 **L** _ _ _   14 **t** _ _ _ _

14

u-e

When you have completed your list of 14 'u-e' words, use each one, once only, to complete the blanks in the sentences below.

1   The man played a happy _____ on his _____.

2   The _____ came to open the new clinic at the beginning of _____.

3   It is easy to _____ a _____ with a donkey.

4   You buy _____ in a bottle, not in a _____.

5   When _____ cheated in the game, his _____ was that he did not understand the_____s.

6   The child _____d to put away the _____s which he had been playing with, and was very _____ to his teacher.

WORDSEARCH PUZZLE - NUMBER 5 | oo

a	b	o	o	t	s	x	j	y
l	m	r	u	s	p	o	o	n
o	o	c	e	h	o	o	t	l
o	o	s	k	r	o	o	m	t
s	n	c	o	o	k	h	w	o
e	d	h	f	w	y	n	o	o
i	p	o	o	l	g	q	o	t
m	j	o	r	o	o	f	d	h
p	z	l	o	o	k	o	s	v

In this wordsearch puzzle you should be able to find 14 'oo' words. Each time you find a word with these letters, write it down - in the right place - in the list below.

1   **b** _ _ _   8   **r** _ _ _

2   **c** _ _ _   9   **r** _ _ _

3   **h** _ _ _   10   **sch** _ _ _

4   **l** _ _ _   11   **sp** _ _ _ _

5   **l** _ _ _ _   12   **sp** _ _ _

6   **m** _ _ _   13   **t** _ _ _ _

7   **p** _ _ _   14   **w** _ _ _

oo

When you have completed your list of 14 'oo' words, use each one, once only, to complete the blanks in the sentences below.

1 The little boy's _____ _____ fell out at _____ .

2 The _____ stirred the gravy with a _____ .

3 We had to put the cases on the _____ rack because there was no _____ in the _____ .

4 The _____ _____ed very beautiful with the _____ reflected in it.

5 As we walked through the dark _____ we could hear owls _____ing, and it felt very _____ .

WORDSEARCH PUZZLE - NUMBER 6 ee

a	t	e	e	t	h	s	k	f
d	k	e	e	p	c	l	n	s
g	i	l	o	s	h	e	e	p
r	s	f	e	e	l	e	e	e
e	t	s	g	q	h	p	m	e
e	e	e	w	h	e	e	l	d
d	e	e	p	s	w	e	e	t
y	r	d	w	e	e	d	j	b
e	b	l	e	e	d	k	v	f

In this wordsearch puzzle you should be able to find 14 'ee' words. Each time you find a word with these letters, write it down - in the right place - in the list below.

1 bl _ _ _

2 f _ _ _

3 gr _ _ _ _

4 k _ _ _

5 k _ _ _

6 s _ _ _

7 sh _ _ _

8 sl _ _ _

9 sp _ _ _

10 st _ _ _

11 sw _ _ _

12 t _ _ _ _

13 w _ _ _

14 wh _ _ _

18

ee

When you have completed your list of 14 'ee' words, use each one, once only, to complete the blanks in the sentences below.

1   The _____ boy ate so much at the party that he began to _____ sick.

2   If you can't _____ , try counting _____!

3   The gardener _____ed the flower bed, and then planted the flower _____s.

4   It is very bad for your _____ to eat too many _____s.

5   He cut his _____ on a sharp stone and it began to _____ badly.

6   If you drive at _____, you must _____ both hands on the _____ing _____.

s	e	a	x	m	e	a	t	r
v	p	e	a	c	h	b	f	b
c	s	g	j	l	e	a	p	e
r	e	v	y	e	a	r	m	a
e	a	e	o	h	u	d	e	t
a	l	a	i	m	x	r	a	p
m	c	l	e	a	r	e	n	w
k	v	n	y	b	e	a	c	h
q	s	c	r	e	a	m	t	z

In this wordsearch puzzle you should be able to find 14 'ea' words. Each time you find a word with these letters, write it down - in the right place - in the list below.

1 b _ _ _ _   8 m _ _ _
2 b _ _ _   9 p _ _ _ _
3 cl _ _ _   10 scr _ _ _
4 cr _ _ _   11 s _ _
5 dr _ _ _   12 s _ _ _
6 l _ _ _   13 v _ _ _
7 m _ _ _   14 y _ _ _

ea

When you have completed your list of 14 'ea' words, use each one, once only, to complete the blanks in the sentences below.

1 I had a _____ that I was lying on a sandy_____.

2 After dinner he had some _____es and _____.

3 If February has 29 days it must be in a _____ _____ .

4 When the athlete began to _____ his opponent, the crowd _____ed and cheered.

5 Pork, beef and _____ are all names of types of _____.

6 The _____ing of the man's speech was not _____ because he spoke too quickly.

7 From the cliff top we could see three _____s swimming in the_____.

WORDSEARCH PUZZLE - NUMBER 8 | oa

d	b	o	a	s	t	v	r	u
g	t	o	a	d	c	o	a	t
r	c	o	a	l	i	i	v	x
o	b	f	s	o	a	p	m	h
a	o	c	l	o	a	k	u	y
n	a	r	j	m	g	j	h	w
m	t	o	q	o	o	o	a	r
l	o	a	f	a	a	k	x	v
p	r	k	s	n	l	o	a	d

In this wordsearch puzzle you should be able to find 14 'oa' words. Each time you find a word with these letters, write it down - in the right place - in the list below.

1 b _ _ _ _

2 b _ _ _

3 cl _ _ _

4 c _ _ _

5 c _ _ _

6 cr _ _ _

7 g _ _ _

8 gr _ _ _

9 l _ _ _

10 l _ _ _

11 m _ _ _

12 o _ _

13 s _ _ _

14 t _ _ _

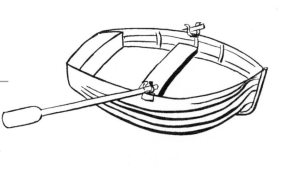

22

oa

When you have completed your list of 14 'oa' words, use each one, once only, to complete the blanks in the sentences below.

1 A _____ is like a _____ without any sleeves.

2 A rowing _____ is no good without _____s.

3 When the teacher mentioned extra homework, the class started to _____ and _____!

4 He went to the shop to buy a _____ of bread and a bar of _____ .

5 The lorry was carrying a heavy _____ of _____ .

6 The boy _____ed that he had scored five _____s.

7 I did not know if the _____ing was coming from a frog or a _____ .

WORDSEARCH PUZZLE - NUMBER 9 | ai

c	l	a	i	m	f	a	i	l
o	m	a	i	n	p	d	k	f
m	c	i	q	n	a	i	l	a
p	t	l	p	a	i	n	S	i
l	r	f	r	s	d	t	p	n
a	a	p	a	i	n	t	a	t
i	i	g	i	v	w	a	i	t
n	n	z	l	r	a	i	n	j
t	s	p	r	a	i	n	h	x

In this wordsearch puzzle you should be able to find 15 'ai' words. One of the words is the name of a country. Each time you find a word with these letters, write it down - in the right place - in the list below.

1 cl _ _ _   9 p _ _ _ _
2 com _ _ _ _ _ _   10 r _ _ _
3 f _ _ _   11 r _ _ _
4 f _ _ _   12 Sp _ _ _
5 m _ _ _   13 spr _ _ _
6 n _ _ _   14 tr _ _ _
7 p _ _ _   15 w _ _ _
8 p _ _ _

ai

When you have completed your list of 15 'ai' words, use each one, once only, to complete the blanks in the sentences below.

1 The _____ from his _____ed ankle made

him _____.

2 It does not _____ so much in the south of

_____ as it does in England.

3 The woman's toe-_____s were _____ed

bright red.

4 There are many _____s from _____

travellers that _____s do not run on time.

5 The workers went on strike because they

_____ed they were not being _____ for

overtime.

6 She _____ed for the bus on the _____

road but it _____ed to turn up.

WORDSEARCH PUZZLE - NUMBER 10 ou

f	o	u	n	d	h	o	u	r
o	b	f	n	m	o	u	t	h
u	j	c	c	o	u	c	h	b
n	p	r	d	u	s	h	k	l
t	r	o	u	s	e	r	s	o
a	o	u	g	e	m	i	q	u
i	u	c	p	o	u	n	d	s
n	d	h	s	h	o	u	t	e
r	o	u	n	d	l	o	u	d

In this wordsearch puzzle you should be able to find 15 'ou' words. Each time you find a word with these letters, write it down - in the right place - in the list below.

1	bl _ _ _ _	9	m _ _ _ _ _
2	c _ _ _ _	10	m _ _ _ _
3	cr _ _ _ _	11	p _ _ _ _
4	f _ _ _ _	12	pr _ _ _
5	f _ _ _ _ _ _ _	13	r _ _ _ _
6	h _ _ _	14	sh _ _ _
7	h _ _ _ _	15	tr _ _ _ _ _ _
8	l _ _ _		

ou

When you have completed your list of 15 'ou' words, use each one, once only, to complete the blanks in the sentences below.

1   We spotted a little grey_____ _____ing

    behind the blue velvet _____.

2   David gave a _____ _____ of pain when

    the ball hit him in the _____.

3   Tom _____ a _____ coin in the middle of

    the _____.

4   It took us nearly an _____ to go _____

    the _____ and garden.

5   She felt very _____ of her new silk _____

    and matching _____.

a	l	l	o	w	e	o	t	g
s	m	c	r	o	w	d	r	r
h	r	o	w	d	y	f	o	o
o	d	w	f	q	u	t	w	w
w	h	e	o	w	l	o	e	l
e	b	r	o	w	n	w	l	t
r	i	g	o	w	n	e	b	o
c	r	o	w	n	k	l	q	w
n	f	l	o	w	e	r	y	n

In this wordsearch puzzle you should be able to find 14 'ow' words. Each time you find a word with these letters, write it down - in the right place - in the list below.

1 **a** _ _ _ _ 　　　8 **gr** _ _ _

2 **br** _ _ _ 　　　9 **o** _ _

3 **c** _ _ _ _ 　　　10 **r** _ _ _ _ _

4 **cr** _ _ _ 　　　11 **sh** _ _ _ _ _

5 **cr** _ _ _ 　　　12 **t** _ _ _ _

6 **fl** _ _ _ _ 　　　13 **t** _ _ _ _

7 **g** _ _ _ 　　　14 **tr** _ _ _ _ _

OW

When you have completed your list of 14 'ow' words, use each one, once only, to complete the blanks in the sentences below.

1 The children were not _____ed to go into

_____ by themselves.

2 After his _____ he dried himself with a _____ .

3 The queen wore a long _____ and had a

_____ on her head.

4 A _____ of _____ teenagers were chanting

and cheering.

5 The dog was _____ing under the table,

_____ing softly.

6 He used a fork and a _____ to loosen the soil in

the _____ beds.

7 We stopped to listen to the hooting of a _____

_____ .

WORDSEARCH PUZZLE - NUMBER 12 | oi

h	p	o	i	s	o	n	g	i	y
s	f	e	k	u	c	o	i	n	q
p	o	d	t	o	i	l	e	t	e
o	i	c	w	j	o	i	n	t	n
i	l	h	m	o	i	s	t	a	o
l	p	o	i	n	t	q	h	v	i
t	i	i	x	g	f	b	v	o	s
e	q	c	d	x	e	o	z	i	e
k	g	e	y	s	o	i	l	d	g
v	c	o	i	l	u	l	z	h	n

In this wordsearch puzzle you should be able to find 14 'oi' words. Each time you find a word with these letters, write it down - in the right place - in the list below.

1 **a** _ _ _ _
2 **b** _ _ _
3 **ch** _ _ _ _ _
4 **c** _ _ _
5 **c** _ _ _
6 **f** _ _ _
7 **j** _ _ _ _

8 **m** _ _ _ _
9 **n** _ _ _ _
10 **p** _ _ _ _
11 **p** _ _ _ _ _
12 **s** _ _ _
13 **sp** _ _ _ _
14 **t** _ _ _ _ _

30

oi

When you have completed your list of 14 'oi' words, use each one, once only, to complete the blanks in the sentences below.

1 Before cooking the _____ of beef, she wrapped it in tin _____ .

2 He ducked down to _____ the _____ous snake which was _____ed on a branch above him.

3 She painted the _____ bright pink.

4 The start of the concert was _____ by the _____ of people talking.

5 After the shower of rain, the _____ was _____ and easy to dig.

6 The little boy _____ed at all the _____s in the fountain.

7 We had a _____ of baked or _____ed potatoes.

WORDSEARCH PUZZLE - NUMBER 13 | aw

e	a	w	f	u	l	i	q	k
d	j	p	h	g	n	a	w	u
r	c	r	a	w	l	b	d	l
a	l	a	w	y	e	r	a	a
w	i	w	k	s	e	a	w	w
e	o	n	u	h	v	w	n	n
r	s	c	r	a	w	l	f	j
f	k	r	z	w	c	l	a	w
q	s	a	w	l	y	a	w	n

In this wordsearch puzzle you should be able to find 15 'aw' words. Each time you find a word with these letters, write it down - in the right place - in the list below.

1 a _ _ _ _   9   l _ _ _
2 br _ _ _   10 l _ _ _ _ _
3 cl _ _   11 pr _ _ _
4 cr _ _ _   12 s _ _
5 d _ _ _   13 scr _ _ _
6 dr _ _ _ _   14 sh _ _ _
7 g _ _ _   15 y _ _ _
8 h _ _ _

32

aw

When you have completed your list of 15 'aw' words, use each one, once only, to complete the blanks in the sentences below.

1 A _____ has sharp _____s called talons.

2 The little mouse _____ed a hole through the wooden _____ with its sharp teeth.

3 The boy's handwriting was so _____ it was little better than a _____.

4 The baby _____ed across the room to see the cats _____ outside.

5 The _____ looked at the menu and ordered a _____ cocktail for starters.

6 When his alarm clock went off at _____, the man stretched and then started to _____.

7 She was sure she _____ an old woman in a black _____ walking across the _____ like a ghost.

33

WORDSEARCH PUZZLE - NUMBER 14 **au**

b	a	s	t	r	o	n	a	u	t
l	a	u	n	d	r	y	f	a	k
d	a	u	t	o	g	r	a	p	h
A	u	g	u	s	t	o	f	p	h
a	d	i	c	a	u	s	e	l	a
u	i	b	g	P	z	j	q	a	u
t	e	x	h	a	u	s	t	u	n
h	n	s	a	u	c	e	r	d	t
o	c	d	k	l	a	u	n	c	h
r	e	x	a	u	t	u	m	n	g

In this wordsearch puzzle you should be able to find 14 'au' words. One of the words is a boy's name. Each time you find a word with these letters, write it down - in the right place - in the list below.

1 **a** _ _ _ _ _ _ _

2 **a** _ _ _ _ _ _ _ _

3 **a** _ _ _ _ _ _ _

4 **A** _ _ _ _ _

5 **a** _ _ _ _ _

6 **a** _ _ _ _ _ _

7 **a** _ _ _ _ _

8 **c** _ _ _ _ _

9 **ex** _ _ _ _ _

10 **h** _ _ _ _ _

11 **l** _ _ _ _ _

12 **l** _ _ _ _ _

13 **P** _ _ _

14 **s** _ _ _ _ _

34

au

When you have completed your list of 14 'au' words, use each one, once only, to complete the blanks in the sentences below.

1 The fumes from car _____ s _____ a lot of pollution.

2 _____ took a pile of dirty washing to the _____ .

3 The well-known _____ was often asked for his _____ .

4 At the end of the concert the _____ _____ ed loudly.

5 The spaceship was _____ ed with three _____ s on board.

6 The end of _____ signals the start of _____ .

7 The man said he didn't believe in flying _____ s or _____ ed houses.

WORDSEARCH PUZZLE - NUMBER 15 ie

d	u	p	r	i	e	s	t	h	v
b	p	i	e	r	c	i	n	g	f
e	s	e	a	x	p	k	q	y	i
l	i	c	s	h	i	e	l	d	e
i	e	e	w	i	e	l	d	w	r
e	g	j	o	t	r	x	z	u	c
f	e	u	v	h	n	i	e	c	e
k	r	e	l	i	e	f	j	w	o
s	h	r	i	e	k	m	q	z	v
c	h	i	e	f	b	r	i	e	f

In this wordsearch puzzle you should be able to find 15 'ie' words. Each time you find a word with these letters, write it down - in the right place - in the list below.

1 b _ _ _ _ _

2 br _ _ _

3 ch _ _ _

4 f _ _ _ _ _

5 n _ _ _ _

6 p _ _ _ _

7 p _ _ _

8 p _ _ _ _ _ _

9 pr _ _ _ _

10 re _ _ _ _

11 sh _ _ _ _

12 shr _ _ _

13 s _ _ _ _

14 th _ _ _

15 w _ _ _ _

36

ie

When you have completed your list of 15 'ie' words, use each one, once only, to complete the blanks in the sentences below.

1 He gave up being a _____ because he lost his

   religious _____ .

2 Before leaving for work, she scribbled a _____

   note to her husband on a _____ of paper.

3 The girl let out a _____ _____ when she saw

   the _____ breaking into the house.

4 It was a great _____ when the _____ ended

   peacefully.

5 I took my nephew and _____ to the _____ as

   a special treat.

6 The tribal _____ was _____ing a spear

   and a _____ , and looked very _____ .

WORDSEARCH PUZZLE - NUMBER 16 $\boxed{\textbf{igh}}$

e	f	l	i	g	h	t	b	f
b	r	i	g	h	t	w	f	j
s	i	l	i	g	h	t	i	o
l	g	n	h	i	g	h	g	h
i	h	i	v	m	i	g	h	t
g	t	g	r	i	g	h	t	i
h	o	h	s	i	g	h	t	g
t	n	t	k	q	s	i	g	h
a	c	d	e	l	i	g	h	t

In this wordsearch puzzle you should be able to find 14 'igh' words. Each time you find a word with these letters, write it down - in the right place - in the list below.

1 **br** _ _ _ _

2 **de** _ _ _ _ _

3 **f** _ _ _ _

4 **fl** _ _ _ _

5 **fr** _ _ _ _

6 **h** _ _ _

7 **l** _ _ _ _

8 **m** _ _ _ _

9 **n** _ _ _ _

10 **r** _ _ _ _

11 **s** _ _ _

12 **s** _ _ _ _

13 **sl** _ _ _ _

14 **t** _ _ _ _ _

igh

When you have completed your list of 14 'igh' words, use each one, once only, to complete the blanks in the sentences below.

1   The stars and moon were so _____ that we had

enough _____ to find our way without torches.

2   At the fair that _____, the big rides gave them a

_____, but the small ones were a _____.

3   The building was so _____ that it looked as if it

_____ fall over in a very strong wind.

4   The _____ from London to New York crossed

_____ over the Atlantic Ocean - a really

beautiful _____.

5   The teacher gave a deep _____ when she saw

boys from her class having a _____.

6   She tried on several jackets in the shop, but much to her

disappointment they were all _____ly too _____.

WORDSEARCH PUZZLE - NUMBER 17 | or

s	h	o	r	t	f	o	r	k
t	q	b	o	r	d	e	r	n
o	r	d	e	r	w	b	n	o
r	i	n	f	o	r	m	o	r
k	Y	v	e	s	t	o	r	m
c	o	r	n	e	r	f	t	a
o	r	n	b	o	r	n	h	l
r	k	e	f	o	r	t	y	z
k	u	m	o	r	n	i	n	g

In this wordsearch puzzle you should be able to find 15 'or' words. One of them is a name of a town. Each time you find a word with these letters, write it down - in the right place - in the list below.

1 b _ _ _ _ _

2 b _ _ _

3 c _ _ _

4 c _ _ _ _ _

5 f _ _ _

6 f _ _ _ _

7 in _ _ _ _ _

8 m _ _ _ _ _ _

9 n _ _ _ _ _

10 n _ _ _ _

11 o _ _ _ _ _

12 sh _ _ _

13 st _ _ _

14 st _ _ _

15 Y _ _ _

40

or

When you have completed your list of 15 'or' words, use each one, once only, to complete the blanks in the sentences below.

1 _____ is in the _____ of England, but it is south of the Scottish _____.

2 In _____ assembly the children were _____ed that school would finish early that day.

3 During the thunder _____ the puppy hid under the table in the _____ of the room.

4 My father was _____ about _____ years ago, so he is much older than me!

5 The commander _____ed his troops to cross the river as a _____-cut.

6 He tried to get the bits of _____ out of the wine bottle with a _____.

7 It is not _____ to stand on one leg unless you are a _____!

s	d	g	f	s	h	a	r	p
n	q	c	a	r	p	e	t	u
a	b	a	r	b	e	r	k	g
r	o	r	m	p	a	r	t	a
l	h	g	e	j	u	y	x	r
b	a	o	r	w	m	a	h	d
a	r	z	s	c	a	r	f	e
r	d	a	r	k	r	d	e	n
k	i	p	a	r	k	v	q	i

In this wordsearch puzzle you should be able to find 15 'ar' words. Each time you find a word with these letters, write it down - in the right place - in the list below.

1 b _ _ _ _ _ _
2 b _ _ _
3 c _ _ _ _ _
4 c _ _ _ _ _
5 d _ _ _
6 f _ _ _ _ _
7 g _ _ _ _ _ _
8 h _ _ _

9 m _ _ _
10 p _ _ _
11 p _ _ _
12 sc _ _ _
13 sh _ _ _
14 sn _ _ _
15 y _ _ _

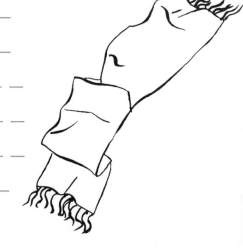

ar

When you have completed your list of 15 'ar' words, use each one, once only, to complete the blanks in the sentences below.

1   The house had no _____, only a back _____ where you could hang washing.

2   By mistake, she left her _____ on the _____ bench.

3   A _____ uses _____ scissors to cut hair.

4   Most people would agree that being a _____ is very _____ work.

5   The dog stopped _____ing, and began to _____ angrily.

6   When the ship sank, only _____ of its _____ was saved.

7   There was a _____ _____ on the _____ where the ink had spilt.

WORDSEARCH PUZZLE - NUMBER 19 ir

c	h	i	r	p	g	i	r	l
a	b	i	r	t	h	d	a	y
g	o	u	t	h	i	r	d	c
c	o	n	f	i	r	m	c	i
b	s	h	i	r	t	s	i	r
i	f	i	r	s	u	k	r	c
r	q	z	k	t	w	i	c	u
d	i	r	t	y	v	r	l	s
z	s	q	u	i	r	t	e	j

In this wordsearch puzzle you should be able to find 14 'ir' words. Each time you find a word with these letters, write it down - in the right place - in the list below.

1 b _ _ _

2 b _ _ _ _ _ _ _

3 ch _ _ _

4 c _ _ _ _ _

5 c _ _ _ _ _

6 con _ _ _ _

7 d _ _ _ _

8 f _ _

9 g _ _ _

10 sh _ _ _

11 sk _ _ _

12 squ _ _ _

13 th _ _ _

14 th _ _ _ _ _

44

When you have completed your list of 14 'ir' words, use each one, once only, to complete the blanks in the sentences below.

1   The clowns in the _____ were _____ing water at each other.

2   The little _____ wore a red jumper and matching _____.

3   After getting lost on the hike with nothing to drink, and walking round in _____s, we at last arrived home feeling hot, tired and _____.

4   When we woke up, we could hear the sound of _____s _____ing in the _____ trees outside.

5   The boy's _____ was so _____ that his mother had to wash it three times to get it clean!

6   I phoned my cousin to _____ that he could come to my _____ party on the _____ of May.

p	e	r	s	o	n	a	h	k
t	h	e	r	m	a	l	d	h
b	g	v	e	r	g	e	h	e
n	j	e	r	s	e	y	e	r
e	x	r	z	w	c	f	r	d
r	e	s	t	e	r	n	b	m
v	y	e	j	r	k	e	r	b
e	s	e	r	v	e	i	q	o
t	e	r	m	e	f	e	r	n

In this wordsearch puzzle you should be able to find 14 'er' words. Each time you find a word with these letters, write it down - in the right place - in the list below.

1 **f** _ _ _
2 **h** _ _ _ _
3 **h** _ _ _
4 **j** _ _ _ _ _
5 **k** _ _ _
6 **n** _ _ _ _
7 **p** _ _ _ _ _ _

8 **re** _ _ _ _ _
9 **s** _ _ _ _
10 **st** _ _ _
11 **sw** _ _ _ _
12 **t** _ _ _
13 **th** _ _ _ _ _
14 **v** _ _ _ _

er

When you have completed your list of 14 'er' words, use each one, once only, to complete the blanks in the sentences below.

1   The car _____d to miss the _____ of cows.

2   The headmaster was a very _____-looking

    _____.

3   When the man _____d the car in his driving-

    test, he hit the _____.

4   The man was wearing a _____ vest, a woollen

    shirt and a thick _____, but he still felt cold.

5   Amongst the _____s on the hillside were wild

    flowers and sweet-smelling _____s.

6   The people who _____d dinner for the children

    only worked during the school _____.

7   He was on the _____ of singing to the crowd, but at

    the last moment he lost his _____.

WORDSEARCH PUZZLE - NUMBER 21 | ur

c	h	u	r	c	h	a	o	m
u	s	u	r	n	a	m	e	u
r	u	b	u	r	g	l	a	r
t	r	u	r	g	e	n	t	d
a	g	r	i	n	j	u	r	e
i	e	n	x	c	q	r	k	r
n	r	t	b	u	r	s	t	c
i	y	p	u	r	s	e	v	f
j	f	u	r	b	h	u	r	l

In this wordsearch puzzle you should be able to find 15 'ur' words. Each time you find a word with these letters, write it down - in the right place - in the list below.

1 **b** _ _ _ _ _ _

2 **b** _ _ _ _ _

3 **b** _ _ _ _ _

4 **ch** _ _ _ _ _

5 **c** _ _ _ _

6 **c** _ _ _ _ _ _ _

7 **f** _ _

8 **h** _ _ _

9 **in** _ _ _ _

10 **m** _ _ _ _ _ _

11 **n** _ _ _ _ _

12 **p** _ _ _ _

13 **s** _ _ _ _ _ _

14 **s** _ _ _ _ _ _

15 **u** _ _ _ _ _ _

48

ur

When you have completed your list of 15 'ur' words, use each one, once only, to complete the blanks in the sentences below.

1 The parish _____ was _____ down in the fire.

2 The woman found her lost _____ behind the _____s in her sitting-room.

3 When the _____d man was brought into hospital, the _____ asked him what his _____ was.

4 The woman _____ into tears when the police told her that her husband had been _____ed.

5 After being taken ill, the man needed _____ _____ to save his life.

6 The man could not _____ his anger when he saw the child _____ a brick at his greenhouse.

7 The _____ stole the woman's _____ coat and jewellery.

WORDSEARCH PUZZLE - NUMBER 22 -ire

e	n	q	u	i	r	e	h	z
x	o	c	q	a	k	n	i	r
p	m	i	n	s	p	i	r	e
i	a	r	e	t	i	r	e	q
r	d	w	f	i	r	e	s	u
e	m	a	g	j	v	b	p	i
b	i	k	d	i	r	e	i	r
l	r	y	e	n	t	i	r	e
p	e	r	s	p	i	r	e	h

In this wordsearch puzzle you should be able to find 12 '-ire' words. Each time you find a word with these letters, write it down - in the right place - in the list below.

1 **ad** _ _ _ _   7 **h** _ _ _

2 **d** _ _ _   8 **in** _ _ _ _ _

3 **en** _ _ _ _ _   9 **per** _ _ _ _ _

4 **en** _ _ _ _   10 **re** _ _ _ _ _

5 **ex** _ _ _ _   11 **re** _ _ _ _

6 **f** _ _ _   12 **s** _ _ _ _

50

-ire

When you have completed your list of 12 '-ire' words, use each one, once only, to complete the blanks in the sentences below.

1 If you are in _____ need, you _____ something very urgently.

2 On the fifth of November the _____ crowd enjoyed watching the _____works.

3 We stopped to _____ the imposing church _____.

4 Before booking the holiday, we _____d about the cost of car- _____.

5 He decided to _____ early to spend more time with his family.

6 The magnificent view _____d her to write a poem.

7 He could not go abroad because his passport had _____d.

8 We _____ when we are too hot, or if we are afraid.

WORDSEARCH PUZZLE - NUMBER 23 -are

i	v	d	s	s	h	a	r	e
p	r	e	p	a	r	e	m	i
v	s	c	a	r	e	h	a	q
C	n	l	r	f	l	a	r	e
l	a	a	e	a	x	r	e	s
a	r	r	z	r	k	e	w	t
r	e	e	h	e	g	o	j	a
e	f	x	g	l	a	r	e	r
a	w	a	r	e	c	a	r	e

In this wordsearch puzzle you should be able to find 15 '-are' words. One of the words is a girl's name. Each time you find a word with these letters, write it down - in the right place - in the list below.

1 a _ _ _ _   9 m _ _ _
2 c _ _ _   10 pre _ _ _ _
3 C _ _ _ _   11 s _ _ _ _
4 de _ _ _ _ _   12 s _ _ _ _
5 f _ _ _   13 s _ _ _ _
6 f _ _ _ _   14 s _ _ _ _
7 g _ _ _ _   15 s _ _ _ _
8 h _ _ _

52

-are

When you have completed your list of 15 '-are' words, use each one, once only, to complete the blanks in the sentences below.

1   A _____ was trapped in the gamekeeper's

   _____.

2   _____ was delighted when her _____ gave

   birth to twin foals, because she had been _____d

   for only one foal, not two.

3   If you _____ at somebody, you _____ at

   them in an unfriendly way.

4   Although the man said he had nothing to _____, the

   Customs Officer was suspicious because he looked

   _____d.

5   After John had spent his allowance on meals and bus-

   _____s, he had no money _____ for anything else.

6   Nobody liked Tom because he never _____d his

   toys or sweets, but Tom didn't seem to_____.

7   The crew of the lifeboat were _____ that the

   men on the life-raft, whom they were trying to rescue,

   had sent up a _____ as a distress signal.

WORDSEARCH PUZZLE - NUMBER 24 -ore

l	i	g	n	o	r	e	g	a
r	m	c	o	r	e	s	p	e
m	p	h	v	y	f	h	o	x
o	l	o	z	q	a	o	r	p
r	o	r	s	n	o	r	e	l
e	r	e	c	x	r	e	j	o
b	e	f	o	r	e	w	g	r
s	t	o	r	e	b	o	r	e
i	a	h	e	s	w	o	r	e

In this wordsearch puzzle you should be able to find 14 '-ore' words. Each time you find a word with these letters, write it down - in the right place - in the list below.

1 be _ _ _ _   8 m _ _ _

2 b _ _ _   9 p _ _ _

3 ch _ _ _   10 s _ _ _ _

4 c _ _ _   11 s _ _ _ _ _

5 ex _ _ _ _ _   12 s _ _ _ _ _

6 ig _ _ _ _   13 s _ _ _ _

7 im _ _ _ _ _   14 s _ _ _ _

54

-ore

When you have completed your list of 14 '-ore' words, use each one, once only, to complete the blanks in the sentences below.

1   The children decided to _____ the rock pools near the sea- _____ .

2   The final goal was _____ d two minutes _____ the end of the match.

3   The man was such a _____ that most people _____ d him at parties.

4   The tired housewife _____ that she would not do any _____ boring household _____ s.

5   The woman _____ d her husband to sleep in the spare room because his loud _____ s prevented her from sleeping.

6   The squirrel had collected a large _____ of nuts and apple _____ s.

7   The _____ s in our skin allow us to sweat.

WORDSEARCH PUZZLE - NUMBER 25 -ll

a	q	c	h	i	l	l	e	h
b	s	t	i	l	l	u	v	f
e	c	d	o	l	l	p	z	u
l	k	r	j	z	s	u	w	l
l	f	i	l	l	p	l	i	l
w	e	l	l	h	i	l	l	t
f	a	l	l	q	l	w	l	x
g	J	i	l	l	l	m	v	s
c	m	b	y	e	l	l	u	

In this wordsearch puzzle you should be able to find 15 '-ll' words. One of the words is a girl's name. Each time you find a word with these letters, write it down - in the right place - in the list below.

1 **b** _ _ _
2 **ch** _ _ _
3 **d** _ _ _
4 **dr** _ _ _
5 **f** _ _ _
6 **f** _ _ _
7 **f** _ _ _
8 **h** _ _ _

9 **J** _ _ _
10 **p** _ _ _
11 **sp** _ _ _
12 **st** _ _ _
13 **w** _ _ _
14 **w** _ _ _
15 **y** _ _ _

56

-ll

When you have completed your list of 15 '-ll' words, use each one, once only, to complete the blanks in the sentences below.

1 When Jack and _____ went up the _____ to fetch some water, they both had a nasty _____!

2 It was _____ raining when we set off, and a _____ wind was blowing.

3 'If you _____ your glass too _____,' said Jane's mum, 'you _____ _____ milk on your dress.'

4 The kind child bought her sister a new _____ because she did not feel very _____.

5 The road-repair team were using a loud _____, so we had to _____ to be heard.

6 To make the church _____s ring, you have to _____ a rope.

WORDSEARCH PUZZLE - NUMBER 26 | -ss

a	i	d	r	e	s	s	h	g
e	m	f	c	h	e	s	s	r
b	o	p	a	s	s	d	q	a
o	s	B	e	s	s	b	u	s
s	s	c	k	g	l	a	s	s
s	f	l	o	s	s	m	g	n
j	u	a	v	p	r	e	s	s
c	s	s	M	i	s	s	y	w
x	s	s	S	w	i	s	s	z

In this wordsearch puzzle you should be able to find 15 '-ss' words. One of the words is a girl's name, one is the name of a nationality and one is a title. Each time you find a word with these letters, write it down - in the right place - in the list below.

1 **B** _ _ _   9 **gr** _ _ _ _

2 **b** _ _ _   10 **m** _ _ _

3 **ch** _ _ _   11 **M** _ _ _

4 **cl** _ _ _   12 **m** _ _ _

5 **dr** _ _ _   13 **p** _ _ _

6 **fl** _ _ _   14 **pr** _ _ _ _

7 **f** _ _ _   15 **Sw** _ _ _

8 **gl** _ _ _

-SS

When you have completed your list of 15 '-ss' words, use each one, once only, to complete the blanks in the sentences below.

1   Tom's new _____ teacher was called _____ Meredith.

2   Susan had a green mark on her _____ where she had been sitting on the damp _____ .

3   Peter could never understand why his mother made such a _____ about the _____ in his room.

4   It is a nice feeling to _____ soft, green _____ against your skin.

5   _____ spent her pocket money on a _____ of Coke and some soft pink candy _____ .

6   Mark was told that if he _____ed his test, he would be given a _____ Army knife as a present.

7   The _____ was very angry when he found two of his office workers playing _____ instead of working.

WORDSEARCH PUZZLE - NUMBER 27 **-ff**

w	o	f	f	s	t	i	f	f
a	y	w	g	h	u	f	f	m
w	r	h	r	s	n	u	f	f
j	u	i	u	c	n	e	x	s
c	f	f	f	l	u	f	f	n
u	f	f	f	i	k	a	z	i
f	b	l	u	f	f	e	e	f
f	q	e	j	f	p	u	f	f
v	k	s	c	r	u	f	f	o

In this wordsearch puzzle you should be able to find 14 '-ff' words. Each time you find a word with these letters, write it down - in the right place - in the list below.

1 **bl** _ _ _

2 **cl** _ _ _ _

3 **c** _ _ _ _

4 **fl** _ _ _

5 **gr** _ _ _

6 **h** _ _ _

7 **o** _ _

8 **p** _ _ _

9 **r** _ _ _

10 **scr** _ _ _

11 **sn** _ _ _ _

12 **sn** _ _ _

13 **st** _ _ _

14 **wh** _ _ _

60

-ff

When you have completed your list of 14 '-ff' words, use each one, once only, to complete the blanks in the sentences below.

1   The man watched birds flying _____ the _____.

2   The dog began to _____ the pink _____ which was coming out of the soft toy.

3   Going up the steep hill made him _____ and _____ and the next day he felt _____ all over.

4   In the time of Queen Elizabeth I, it was the fashion to wear long dresses with frilly _____s and tight _____s round the neck.

5   If you _____ somebody, you fool them into believing something which is not true.

6   After one _____ of the strong _____, the man began to sneeze violently.

7   To play the part of the villain in the school play, he had to dress in _____y clothes and speak in a _____ voice.

WORDSEARCH PUZZLE - NUMBER 28 -ck

l	b	c	e	b	r	i	c	k
o	x	B	l	a	c	k	d	p
c	t	r	u	c	k	e	J	i
k	d	u	c	k	j	f	a	c
s	i	z	k	s	t	u	c	k
t	q	u	a	c	k	y	k	s
a	n	e	c	k	q	h	e	i
c	l	o	c	k	e	q	w	c
k	x	w	h	s	h	o	c	k

In this wordsearch puzzle you should be able to find 16 '-ck' words. One of the words is a surname. Each time you find a word with these letters, write it down - in the right place - in the list below.

1 b _ _ _   9 n _ _ _

2 Bl _ _ _   10 p _ _ _

3 br _ _ _   11 qu _ _ _

4 cl _ _ _   12 sh _ _ _

5 d_ _ _   13 s _ _ _ _

6 J _ _ _   14 st _ _ _

7 l _ _ _   15 st _ _ _

8 l _ _ _   16 tr _ _ _ _

62

-ck

When you have completed your list of 16 '-ck' words, use each one, once only, to complete the blanks in the sentences below.

1 The _____s in the pond began to _____ madly when the children threw the bread crumbs in the water.

2 Mr. _____ got the _____ of his life when he won a grandfather _____.

3 _____'s mother kept him off school because he had a stiff _____, a headache and felt _____.

4 The thief found it easy to _____ the _____s of most car doors.

5 Mr. Jenkin's bad _____ was to get _____ in a traffic jam on the way to the football match.

6 The men were told to unload the _____s from the _____, and to _____ them at the _____ of the shed.

WORDSEARCH PUZZLE - NUMBER 29 -dge

a	b	r	i	d	g	e	e	d
f	u	d	g	e	h	f	d	r
r	d	c	s	l	e	d	g	e
i	g	a	l	j	d	i	e	d
d	e	n	u	d	g	e	q	g
g	j	u	d	g	e	y	i	e
e	a	f	g	b	a	d	g	e
h	x	u	e	l	o	d	g	e
m	t	r	u	d	g	e	z	v

In this wordsearch puzzle you should be able to find 14 '-dge' words. Each time you find a word with these letters, write it down - in the right place - in the list below.

1   **b** _ _ _ _

2   **br** _ _ _ _

3   **b** _ _ _ _

4   **dr** _ _ _

5   **e** _ _ _

6   **fr** _ _ _

7   **f** _ _ _ _

8   **h** _ _ _ _

9   **j** _ _ _ _

10   **l** _ _ _ _

11   **n** _ _ _ _

12   **sl** _ _ _

13   **sl** _ _ _

14   **tr** _ _ _ _

-dge

When you have completed your list of 14 '-dge' words, use each one, once only, to complete the blanks in the sentences below.

1   The children had to _____ a long way through deep snow, dragging their _____s before they found a good slope.

2   When they _____d the bottom of the river, they found a rusty old _____!

3   When Simon _____d his friend Mark because he had dozed off in the French lesson, Mark fell off the _____ of his chair.

4   The _____ which Lee had made in the cookery lesson looked like a thick _____.

5   A complaint was _____d against the _____ for taking bribes.

6   The boys tried to heave the heavy rock off the _____, but they could not _____ it.

7   Daniel found his lost _____ under the holly _____.

WORDSEARCH PUZZLE - NUMBER 30 -tch

s	c	r	a	t	c	h	q	D
n	c	l	u	t	c	h	f	u
a	a	p	i	t	c	h	e	t
t	t	a	b	m	g	s	t	c
c	c	t	S	c	o	t	c	h
h	h	c	m	a	t	c	h	i
j	q	h	d	i	t	c	h	t
n	b	a	t	c	h	k	u	c
l	a	t	c	h	u	t	c	h

In this wordsearch puzzle you should be able to find 15 '-tch' words. One of the words is the name of a nationality. Each time you find a word with these letters, write it down - in the right place - in the list below.

1 b _ _ _ _ _
2 c _ _ _ _ _
3 cl _ _ _ _ _
4 d _ _ _ _ _
5 D _ _ _ _ _
6 f _ _ _ _ _
7 h _ _ _ _ _
8 h _ _ _ _ _

9 l _ _ _ _ _
10 m _ _ _ _ _
11 p _ _ _ _ _
12 p _ _ _ _ _
13 Sc _ _ _ _ _
14 scr _ _ _ _ _
15 sn _ _ _ _ _

66

-tch

When you have completed your list of 15 '-tch' words, use each one, once only, to complete the blanks in the sentences below.

1   The football _____ was cancelled because the

_____ was waterlogged.

2   The escaped convict tried to _____ a lift to the

_____ border, hoping that the police would not

_____ him.

3   The rabbit went missing because somebody had

left the door of its _____ off the _____.

4   The child had a _____ of red skin on his arm

which made him _____ all the time.

5   We were surprised to see a full bottle of _____

lying at the bottom of the _____.

6   The man asked his son to _____ a _____ of

fresh eggs from the farm.

7   Although the woman was _____ing her handbag

tight, a thief still managed to _____ it.

ANSWERS TO WORDSEARCH PUZZLES

NUMBER 1 (a-e)

1	cake	8	lake
2	crane	9	late
3	crate	10	made
4	Dave	11	name
5	escape	12	same
6	gate	13	wade
7	Jane	14	wake

Sentences

1	wake	late	
2	Jane	made	cake
3	gate	escape	
4	same	name	
5	Dave	wade	lake
6	crane	crate	

NUMBER 2 (i-e)

1	bike	9	pine
2	bite	10	ride
3	bride	11	ripe
4	five	12	slide
5	hide	13	time
6	kite	14	white
7	Mike	15	wife
8	nine		

Sentences

1	time	slide	
2	five	nine	
3	bride	white	
4	ride	bike	
5	kite	pine	
6	wife	hide	
7	Mike	bite	ripe

NUMBER 3 (o-e)

1	broke	9	Pope
2	code	10	rode
3	doze	11	Rome
4	hole	12	slope
5	mole	13	smoke
6	nose	14	stove
7	note	15	woke
8	phone		

Sentences

1	mole	hole	
2	broke	nose	
3	Pope	Rome	
4	smoke	stove	
5	note	code	
6	doze	woke	phone
7	rode	slope	

NUMBER 4 (u-e)

1	confuse	8	mule
2	cube	9	perfume
3	Duke	10	refuse
4	excuse	11	rude
5	flute	12	rule
6	June	13	tube
7	Luke	14	tune

Sentences

1	tune	flute	
2	Duke	June	
3	confuse	mule	
4	perfume	tube	
5	Luke	excuse	rule
6	refuse	cube	rude

NUMBER 5 (oo)

1	boot	8	roof
2	cook	9	room
3	hoot	10	school
4	look	11	spooky
5	loose	12	spoon
6	moon	13	tooth
7	pool	14	wood

Sentences

1	loose	tooth	school
2	cook	spoon	
3	roof	room	boot
4	pool	look	moon
5	wood	hoot	spooky

NUMBER 6 (ee)

1	bleed	8	sleep
2	feel	9	speed
3	greedy	10	steer
4	keep	11	sweet
5	knee	12	teeth
6	seed	13	weed
7	sheep	14	wheel

Sentences

1	greedy	feel		
2	sleep	sheep		
3	weed	seed		
4	teeth	sweet		
5	knee	bleed		
6	speed	keep	steer	wheel

NUMBER 7 (ea)

1	beach	8	meat
2	beat	9	peach
3	clear	10	scream
4	cream	11	sea
5	dream	12	seal
6	leap	13	veal
7	mean	14	year

Sentences

1	dream	beach
2	peach	cream
3	leap	year
4	beat	scream
5	veal	meat
6	mean	clear
7	seal	sea

NUMBER 8 (oa)

1	boast	8	groan
2	boat	9	load
3	cloak	10	loaf
4	coal	11	moan
5	coat	12	oar
6	croak	13	soap
7	goal	14	toad

Sentences

1	cloak	coat
2	boat	oar
3	moan	groan
4	loaf	soap
5	load	coal
6	boast	goal
7	croak	toad

NUMBER 9 (ea)

1	claim	9	paint
2	complaint	10	rail
3	fail	11	rain
4	faint	12	Spain
5	main	13	sprain
6	nail	14	train
7	paid	15	wait
8	pain		

Sentences

1	pain	sprain	faint
2	rain	Spain	
3	nail	paint	
4	complaint	rail	train
5	claim	paid	
6	wait	main	fail

NUMBER10 (ou)

1	blouse	9	mouse
2	couch	10	mouth
3	crouch	11	pound
4	found	12	proud
5	fountain	13	round
6	hour	14	shout
7	house	15	trousers
8	loud		

Sentences

1	mouse	crouch	couch
2	loud	shout	mouth
3	found	pound	fountain
4	hour	round	house
5	proud	blouse	trousers

NUMBER 11 (ow)

1	allow	8	growl
2	brown	9	owl
3	cower	10	rowdy
4	crowd	11	shower
5	crown	12	towel
6	flower	13	town
7	gown	14	trowel

Sentences

1	allow	town
2	shower	towel
3	gown	crown
4	crowd	rowdy
5	cower	growl
6	trowel	flower
7	brown	owl

NUMBER 12 (oi)

1	avoid	8	moist
2	boil	9	noise
3	choice	10	point
4	coil	11	poison
5	coin	12	soil
6	foil	13	spoilt
7	joint	14	toilet

Sentences

1	joint	foil	
2	avoid	poison	coil
3	toilet		
4	spoilt	noise	
5	soil	moist	
6	point	coin	
7	choice	boil	

NUMBER13 (aw)

1	awful	9	lawn
2	brawl	10	lawyer
3	claw	11	prawn
4	crawl	12	saw
5	dawn	13	scrawl
6	drawer	14	shawl
7	gnaw	15	yawn
8	hawk		

Sentences

1	hawk	claw	
2	gnaw	drawer	
3	awful	scrawl	
4	crawl	brawl	
5	lawyer	prawn	
6	dawn	yawn	
7	saw	shawl	lawn

NUMBER14 (au)

1	applaud	8	cause
2	astronaut	9	exhaust
3	audience	10	haunt
4	August	11	launch
5	author	12	laundry
6	autograph	13	Paul
7	autumn	14	saucer

Sentences

1	exhaust	cause
2	Paul	laundry
3	author	autograph
4	audience	applaud
5	launch	astronaut
6	August	autumn
7	saucer	haunt

NUMBER 15 (ie)

1	belief	9	priest
2	brief	10	relief
3	chief	11	shield
4	fierce	12	shriek
5	niece	13	siege
6	piece	14	thief
7	pier	15	wield
8	piercing		

Sentences

1	priest	belief		
2	brief	piece		
3	piercing	shriek	thief	
4	relief	siege		
5	niece	pier		
6	chief	wield	shield	fierce

NUMBER 16 (igh)

1	bright	8	might
2	delight	9	night
3	fight	10	right
4	flight	11	sigh
5	fright	12	sight
6	high	13	slight
7	light	14	tight

Sentences

1	bright	light	
2	night	fright	delight
3	high	might	
4	flight	right	sight
5	sigh	fight	
6	slight	tight	

NUMBER 17 (or)

1	border	9	normal
2	born	10	north
3	cork	11	order
4	corner	12	short
5	fork	13	stork
6	forty	14	storm
7	inform	15	York
8	morning		

Sentences

1	York	north	border
2	morning	inform	
3	storm	corner	
4	born	forty	
5	order	short	
6	cork	fork	
7	normal	stork	

NUMBER 18 (ar)

1	barber	9	mark
2	bark	10	park
3	cargo	11	part
4	carpet	12	scarf
5	dark	13	sharp
6	farmer	14	snarl
7	gardern	15	yard
8	hard		

Sentences

1	garden	yard	
2	scarf	park	
3	barber	sharp	
4	farmer	hard	
5	bark	snarl	
6	part	cargo	
7	dark	mark	carpet

NUMBER 19 (ir)

1	bird	8	fir
2	birthday	9	girl
3	chirp	10	shirt
4	circle	11	skirt
5	circus	12	squirt
6	confirm	13	third
7	dirty	14	thirsty

Sentences

1	circus	squirt	
2	girl	skirt	
3	circle	thirsty	
4	bird	chirp	fir
5	shirt	dirty	
6	confirm	birthday	third

NUMBER 20 (ur)

1	fern	8	reverse
2	herb	9	serve
3	herd	10	stern
4	jersey	11	swerve
5	kerb	12	term
6	nerve	13	thermal
7	person	14	verge

Sentences

1	swerve	herd
2	stern	person
3	reverse	kerb
4	thermal	jersey
5	fern	herb
6	serve	term
7	verge	nerve

NUMBER 21 (ur)

1	burglar	9	injure
2	burnt	10	murder
3	burst	11	nurse
4	church	12	purse
5	curb	13	surgery
6	curtain	14	surname
7	fur	15	urgent
8	hurl		

Sentences

1	church	burnt	
2	purse	curtains	
3	injure	nurse	surname
4	burst	murder	
5	urgent	surgery	
6	curb	hurl	
7	burglar	fur	

NUMBER 22 (-ire)

1	admire	7	hire
2	dire	8	inspire
3	enquire	9	perspire
4	entire	10	require
5	expire	11	retire
6	fire	12	spire

Sentences

1	dire	require
2	entire	fire
3	admire	spire
4	enquire	hire
5	retire	
6	inspire	
7	expire	
8	perspire	

NUMBER 23 (-are)

1	aware	9	mare
2	care	10	prepare
3	Clare	11	scare
4	declare	12	share
5	fare	13	snare
6	flare	14	spare
7	glare	15	stare
8	hare		

Sentences

1	hare	snare	
2	Clare	mare	prepare
3	glare	stare	
4	declare	scare	
5	fare	spare	
6	share	care	
7	aware	flare	

NUMBER 24 (-ore)

1	before	8	more
2	bore	9	pore
3	chore	10	score
4	core	11	shore
5	explore	12	snore
6	ignore	13	store
7	implore	14	swore

Sentences

1	explore	shore	
2	score	before	
3	bore	ignore	
4	swore	more	chore
5	implore	snore	
6	store	core	
7	pore		

NUMBER 25 (-ll)

1	bell	9	Jill
2	chill	10	pull
3	doll	11	spill
4	drill	12	still
5	fall	13	well
6	fell	14	will
7	fill	15	yell
8	hill		

Sentences

1	Jill	hill	fall	
2	still	chill		
3	fill	full	will	spill
4	doll	well		
5	drill	yell		
6	bell	pull		

NUMBER 26 (-ss)

1	Bess	9	grass
2	boss	10	mess
3	chess	11	Miss
4	class	12	moss
5	dress	13	pass
6	floss	14	press
7	fuss	15	Swiss
8	glass		

Sentences

1	class	Miss	
2	dress	grass	
3	fuss	mess	
4	press	moss	
5	Bess	glass	floss
6	pass	Swiss	
7	boss	chess	

NUMBER 27 (-ff)

1	bluff	8	puff
2	cliff	9	ruff
3	cuff	10	scruff
4	fluff	11	sniff
5	gruff	12	snuff
6	huff	13	stiff
7	off	14	whiff

Sentences

1	off	cliff	
2	sniff	fluff	
3	huff	puff	stiff
4	cuff	ruff	
5	bluff		
6	whiff	snuff	
7	scruff	gruff	

NUMBER 28 (-ck)

1	back	9	neck
2	Black	10	pick
3	brick	11	quack
4	clock	12	shock
5	duck	13	sick
6	Jack	14	stack
7	lock	15	stuck
8	luck	16	truck

Sentences

1	duck	quack		
2	Black	shock	clock	
3	Jack	neck	sick	
4	pick	lock		
5	luck	stuck		
6	brick	truck	stack	back

NUMBER 29 (-dge)			
1	badge	8	hedge
2	bridge	9	judge
3	budge	10	lodge
4	dredge	11	nudge
5	edge	12	sledge
6	fridge	13	sludge
7	fudge	14	trudge

Sentences

1	trudge	sledge
2	dredge	fridge
3	nudge	edge
4	fudge	sludge
5	lodge	judge
6	bridge	budge
7	badge	hedge

NUMBER 30 (-tch)			
1	batch	9	latch
2	catch	10	match
3	clutch	11	patch
4	ditch	12	pitch
5	Dutch	13	Scotch
6	fetch	14	scratch
7	hitch	15	snatch
8	hutch		

Sentences

1	match	pitch	
2	hitch	Dutch	catch
3	hutch	latch	
4	patch	scratch	
5	Scotch	ditch	
6	fetch	batch	
7	clutch	snatch	

TAKE TIME

Movement exercises for parents, teachers and therapists of children with difficulties in speaking, reading, writing and spelling. By Mary Nash-Wortham and Jean Hunt.

Take Time tackles some of the root causes of difficulties in speaking, reading, writing and spelling - especially where there is a lack of co-ordination, rhythm and timing.

The innovative movement exercises, based on curative eurythmy, and the other activities described can be tailored specifically to individual situations. This has resulted in the considerable popularity of this book and its recommendation by all the major dyslexia organisations.

Take Time features:

• *Pointers* to clarify areas of difficulty:

  - Timing and Rhythm
  - Direction
  - Spatial Orientation and Movement
  - Sequencing
  - Laterality
  - Fine Motor Control for Speech, Writing and Reading

• General *exercises,* including 'warm-ups'.

• Specific *exercises* to help with particular areas of difficulty and individual situations.

• Descriptions of useful resource *equipment.*

"To my mind no therapist or remedial teacher should be without this edition by their side."

From the foreword by Dr. Beve Hornsby PhD, MSc, MEd, MCST, ABPsS
Consultant Speech Therapist and Clinical Psychologist.

ISBN 1 869981 50 2   106 pages   £8.95

Value Your Voice!

By Mary Nash-Wortham.

In today's society, everybody has to communicate - constantly! There are many ways to do so: We write, we gesture, we whistle, we press buttons - but the most important route is, of course, our voice.

We use the voice to persuade, to describe, to enthuse, to move our audience, to make them laugh, to make them perform... But do *you* ever give enough thought, protection and care to this vital and precious asset?

If you rely on clear, audible, authoritative and interesting expression to speak with friends and colleagues, to present yourself to clients, to lecture students or teach classes then this book will be invaluable to *you!*

Information on speech production is combined with simple but effective exercises to keep your voice on top form. This 'learning' and 'doing' can help even the most croaky speaker to understand why their speech may be failing *and to make some real improvements!*

All of us - especially teachers - know that a fit, healthy voice is essential to our daily lives, especially at work. *Value Your Voice!* will help you enhance your skills of effective communication and create a voice that does what you want and - crucially - when you want it!

ISBN 1 869981 55 3   50 pages   £6.95

PHONIC RHYME TIME

A unique collection of phonic rhymes for precise practice in
speaking and reading. By Mary Nash-Wortham.

Devised for all teachers, therapists and students of speech.
Over 200 original and traditional rhymes, verses and phrases.
All phonic positions - initial, medial and final - are covered
independently.
Sound blends for beginning, middle and end of words.
Separate vowel sound exercises.
Spiral bound for convenient use.

Phonic Rhyme Time solves the problem often met by teachers:
finding memorable rhymes which concentrate solely on one specific
sound. Many standard rhymes actually contain similar though
different sounds and this can lead to considerable confusion. In
contrast, every rhyme, verse or phrase in *Phonic Rhyme Time* has
been selected or developed precisely because it is dedicated to just
one sound.

The book also describes how speech sounds are produced and illustrates consonant and vowel positions.
It is invaluable in general language teaching as an extension of vocabulary and spelling work, and for
remedial or special needs teaching. The wide range of rhymes and verses means it is suitable for both
children and adults. The clear presentation enables easy selection and varied use of the rhymes.

*"This collection of intelligent rhymes for each sound - and one in which the concentration of sound in
each rhyme is so strong - is an invaluable tool for every teacher and student...   I have found Phonic
Rhyme Time enormously illuminating and thought-provoking. I commend it to you without
reservation."*

From the Foreword by Shaun McKenna., Principal of Examinations, LAMDA.

ISBN 1 869981 47 2   77 pages   £9.95

THE EXTRA LESSON

Exercises in movement, drawing and painting to help children with difficulties in writing, reading and arithmetic.
By Audrey E McAllen.

The Extra Lesson brings together the experience of the author and her many teacher colleagues in
Waldorf (or Steiner) schools world-wide in helping children to overcome their specific learning difficulties,
and provides an initial insight into the 'holistic' approach adopted in these schools.

The book provides an invaluable sequence of practical, well-proven activities and exercises with which to
observe the problems encountered by the individual child and from which a suitable remedial programme
can be composed. It does not attempt to detail all underlying causes of learning difficulty but provides the
reader with sufficient background to appreciate the effect of each exercise.

The author's experience is borne out by the latest research in many associated disciplines. This indicates
that if any of the basic stages of the first seven years development are missed out or are not completed
then the pupil's potential for learning diminishes and his progress in his class or in a remedial situation is
unlikely to be maintained. It is the recognition of these gaps in development and their subsequent
recapitulation and integration that are addressed by the suggested diagnostic exercises in this book. Once
these stages, common to the development of all children, are completed the teacher can then continue to
support the pupil according to their specific individual needs.

ISBN 1 869981 06 5   123 pages   £11.95